The BAMBURGH SERPENT

Illustrated by Jorge Lulić

Published by:
Keepdate (Publishing) Ltd,
21 Portland Terrace, Jesmond,
Newcastle upon Tyne NE2 1QQ.

Illustrations copyright © 1993 Jorge Lulić

First edition 1989
Second edition 1993

ISBN 0-9520494-8-1

O, laydown your sword, unbend
    your bow,
And give me kisses three,
For though I am a poisonous
    worm,
No harm I'll do to thee.

O, laydown your sword, unbend
    your bow,
And give me kisses three,
If I'm not changed before the
    sun goes down,
Then changed I'll never be.

Bamburgh Castle in Northumberland was once the home of a sad widower king. One day the King's son Childy Wynd decided to leave home to seek his fortune in a far away land.

His daughter, Margaret, was the lady of Bamburgh. She was the most beautiful girl in the land. Her hair was the colour of golden corn and her eyes were as blue as the bluebells in the meadow.

All of the people of Bamburgh loved her for she had the sweetest voice and when she danced, she danced like the waves of the sea.

But one day her father, the King, met a lady who made him forget his dead wife. The old King was bewitched by her beauty and her enchanting ways.

nd so the King married the enchantress and there was a splendid procession through the streets of Bamburgh to welcome the new Queen. Although she was beautiful to see, for every look the crowd gave her, they gave Margaret three.

oon the time came for Margaret to hand over the keys of the castle to the new Queen. As the Queen took them she overheard some of the castle ladies whispering, "The Queen is lovely but Margaret is three times more lovelier than any other lady I have ever seen".
At that moment the Queen promised herself that she would get rid of Margaret.

A few days later Margaret disappeared. The people of Bamburgh and everyone in the castle were very sad. They all searched for Margaret but at last they thought she had drowned.

Only the Witch queen, for she was a witch, knew that Margaret had been turned into a serpent and was lying asleep in the woods near Spindlestone rock.

owever a few months passed and the queen began to worry and regret her evil deed . . .

. . . because by this time the serpent
had grown enormous, so big that it could
wind itself around the castle rock and
was destroying everything in its path.

he Queen tried all of her magic spells but none could stop the serpent.

At last the King's son, Childy Wynd heard about the serpent and decided to return home and get rid of the monster.

he Queen fearing she would be found out, cast a spell to call up storms to keep Childy Wynd from landing on the shores of Northumberland.

Three times he tried to reach the shore and three times he was tossed and turned away by the waves.

"This is witchcraft" said Childy. But one of the sailors on his ship told him that he must build a new ship.

he sailor told Childy that the ship must be built of rowan wood with a sail as red as a rowanberry to break the witches spell.

The new ship sailed safely into Buddle Bay and Childy Wynd leapt out of the ship and over the dunes where the serpent was waiting.

Bravely, Childy raised his sword, about to kill the serpent, when it spoke:

> O, laydown your sword, unbend your bow,
> And give me kisses three,
> For though I am a poisonous worm,
> No harm I'll do to thee.
>
> O, laydown your sword, unbend your bow,
> And give me kisses three,
> If I'm not changed before the sun goes down,
> Then changed I'll never be.

hildy was astonished and felt he could never kiss such a monster. But, as he looked into its eyes he saw that the serpent was sad.
Laying down his sword he kissed the serpent once, twice, three times . . .

After the third kiss the serpent began to change before him and in its place stood his beautiful sister Margaret.

ogether they returned to the castle and there they found the Witch Queen helping herself to a feast. "You evil witch", cried Childy "it was you who transformed Margaret into a horrible serpent and for your punishment you shall be turned into an ugly hopping toad!"

All that was left of the witch was a big ugly toad. And the legend goes that the sad ugly toad still hides at the bottom of the castle well and to this day it comes out sometimes to frighten the unwary passers by.